Contents

Section 1 Test 1

A

		ANSWER
1	6 + 4 + 8	
2	15p − 8p	p
3	$\frac{1}{2}$ hour = ☐ min	min
4	5p + 5p + 2p + 2p	p
5	$\frac{1}{2}$ of 14	
6	5 TWOS = ☐ FIVES	FIVES
7	5 + 9 = 10 + ☐	
8	3 + ☐ = 12	
9	7 cm + 8 cm = 10 cm + ☐ cm	cm
10	6 × 2 = 3 × ☐	

B

		ANSWER
1	Add 5, 4 and 9.	
2	Subtract 7 from 16.	
3	Find the sum of 10p, 5p and 2 TWOS.	p
4	How many FIVES are worth 20p?	FIVES
5	Increase 17 by 8.	
6	How much more than 9p are 3 TWOS and a FIVE?	p
7	1 hour = 30 min + ☐ min	min
8	How many halves in 9 whole ones?	
9	Three times the value of a coin equals 15p. What is the value of the coin?	p
10	How many metres are there in (a) 1 km (b) $\frac{1}{2}$ km?	(a) m (b) m

C

		ANSWER
1	What is the sixth letter of the alphabet?	
2	How many days are there in three weeks?	
3	A strip 18 cm long is cut in half. How long is one of the pieces?	cm
4	Six sweets are taken from a box of 20. How many are left?	
5	If one coin is taken from the box below, 11p is left. Write the value of the coin.	p

		ANSWER
6	Which two coins must be added to the five coins in the box above to make a total of 20p?	p | p
7	Find the difference in length between the longest and the shortest of the lines below.	cm

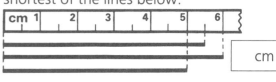

		ANSWER
8	Amy had 18p. She spent 9p and 5p. How much had she left?	p
9	 The dial shows the amount of petrol left in a tank. What fraction of the full tank has been used?	
10	Josh has 12p. How much more does he need to buy 4 boxes at 5p each?	p

Section 1   Test 2

A
		ANSWER
1	$\frac{1}{2}$ of 20	
2	10p + 6p + 3p	p
3	8 TWOS = 1 TEN + p	p
4	14 ÷ 2	
5	$\frac{1}{4}$ hour = min	min
6	9 + 7 = 6 +	
7	9 cm × 2 = 10 cm + cm	cm
8	4p + 9p − 7p	p
9	10 ÷ 2 = 10 −	
10	15p − p = 6p	p

B
		ANSWER
1	Multiply 4 by 8.	
2	Divide 18 by 3.	
3	Write the eighth month of the year.	
4	Find the sum of a TEN and 3 FIVES.	p
5	How many minutes from 11.05 a.m. to 11.45 a.m.?	min
6	One quarter of 20	
7	Subtract 16p from 25p.	p
8	How many half metres together measure $4\frac{1}{2}$ m?	
9	7 × 4 = 30 −	
10	What is the total of 6p, 3p and 8p?	p

C
		ANSWER
1	James is 9. How old will he be in 8 years time?	
2	What number must be added to 8 to make 20?	
3	How many TENS have the same value as these coins?	TENS

4. Tom had 28p. He gave a quarter of his money to Amy. How much had he left? [ ] p

5.

Which of the shapes is
(a) a square
(b) a rectangle?   (a) [ ] (b) [ ]

6. What is the sum of the even numbers between 3 and 9? [ ]

7. What is the total length of eight strips like this?
   [ ] cm

8. How many 5p sweets can be bought for 1 TWENTY, 1 TEN and 1 FIVE? [ ]

9. Which four coins together equal 18p? [ ]p [ ]p [ ]p [ ]p

10.  Write in figures the time $2\frac{1}{2}$ h later. Use a.m. or p.m. [ ]

Section 1 Test 3

ANSWER

1   4 TWOS = 1 FIVE + ☐ p   ☐ p

2 $\frac{1}{2}$ hour + 10 min   ☐ min

3   8 + 7 − 10   ☐

4   (a) 1 litre = ☐ mℓ   (a) ☐ mℓ
     (b) $\frac{1}{2}$ litre = ☐ mℓ   (b) ☐ mℓ

5   10p + 2p + 2p − 7p   ☐ p

6   ☐ + 7 = 15   ☐

7   5p + 7p = 1 TEN + ☐ p   ☐ p

8   2 kg × 7 = 10 kg + ☐ kg   ☐ kg

9   16 − ☐ = 9   ☐

10   8 ÷ 2 = 16 ÷ ☐   ☐

ANSWER

1   Multiply 4 by 7.   ☐

2   How many minutes from 8.55 a.m. to 9.05 a.m.?   ☐ min

3   Decrease 20p by 11p.   ☐ p

4   Four groups of 4. How many altogether?   ☐

5   How many metres are there in
(a) 200 cm
(b) 500 cm?   (a) ☐ m   (b) ☐ m

6   What is one fifth of thirty?   ☐

7   Find the sum of $4\frac{1}{2}$, $7\frac{1}{2}$ and 6.   ☐

8   Subtract 9 from 26.   ☐

9 $1 - \frac{1}{10}$ ☐

10   Which 3 coins together make 9p?   ☐ p   ☐ p   ☐ p

ANSWER

1 | First of January 1983 |
Write this date using figures only.   ☐ ☐ ☐

2   Which number is 10 times greater than 6?   ☐

3   Find the change from a TEN and 2 FIVES after spending 16p.   ☐ p

4   Which number is midway between 10 and 20?   ☐

5   What fraction of the circle is not shaded?   ☐

6   34 children are asked to stand in groups of 5. How many children are left over?   ☐

7   Find the difference between a quarter of 16p and a half of 16p.   ☐ p

8 | SCHOOL TIMES |
| 9 a.m. to noon |
| 1.30 p.m. to 4 p.m. |
How many hours is the school day?   ☐ h

9
cm   1   2   3   4   5   6
If each cm on the line represents 4 metres, what length does the whole line represent?   ☐ m

10 | 3   4   5   6   7 |
Which two of these numbers will divide into 35 without a remainder?   ☐ ☐

Section 1 Test 4

A
		ANSWER
1	$\frac{1}{2}$ hour − 10 min	min
2	10p + 2p + 1p − 6p	p
3	$\frac{1}{3}$ of 18 kg	kg
4	3 × 9 = 9 + 9 +	
5	6 + 8 = 10 +	
6	18 − 9 = 12 −	
7	10 × 2 = 5 ×	
8	3 TENS = ⬜ FIVES	FIVES
9	3 FIVES − ⬜ p = 9p	p
10	3 TWOS + 1 FIVE + ⬜ p = 15p	p

B
		ANSWER
1	How much less is 7 TWOS than 1 TWENTY?	p
2	Find the product of 6 and 6.	
3	One tenth of a FIFTY.	p
4	From the total of 4, 5 and 6 subtract 7.	
5	Find the value of 4 times $4\frac{1}{2}$.	
6	How many cm are there in (a) 2 m (b) $3\frac{1}{2}$ m?	(a) cm / (b) cm
7	20 plus 3 minus 8	
8	How many grams are there in (a) 1 kg (b) $\frac{1}{2}$ kg?	(a) g / (b) g
9	Find the difference between (8 + 9) and 27.	
10	Twenty quarters. How many whole ones is that?	

C
		ANSWER
1	36 sweets — How many children can be given 4 sweets each from this bag?	
2	1 TWENTY and 1 FIVE. How much more to make 31p?	p
3	How many minutes from ten minutes to ten to quarter past ten?	min
4	Which coin is worth ten times more than a FIVE?	_____
5	Amy saves 5p each week. How many weeks will it take her to save 45p?	
6	4 cm / 8 cm — What is the total length of the four sides of this rectangle?	cm
7	Which 2 coins are given in change after spending 25p from 50p?	p | p
8	One box has a mass of $1\frac{1}{2}$ kg. What is the mass of 8 of the boxes?	kg
9	How many FIVES have the same value as the sum of 2 TENS and 10 TWOS?	FIVES
10	Sweets cost 9p each. Tom has 40p. How much more does he need to buy 5 sweets?	p

Section 1 Test 5

A

		ANSWER
1	$5 + 6 + 7 = 10 +$	
2	$1 \text{ kg } 700 \text{ g} = \quad \text{g}$	g
3	$7 \times 4 = 20 +$	
4	$44 - 9$	
5	$3 + 9 = 8 +$	
6	$4 \times 9 = \quad$ tens + 6 units	tens
7	$20p + 5p - 6p$	p
8	5 TENS = $\quad$ FIVES	FIVES
9	$25 \div 4 = \quad$ rem.	rem.
10	$5p + 2p + 10p - \quad p = 9p$	p

B

		ANSWER
1	500 plus 80 plus 4	
2	Multiply 8 by 6.	
3	Share 24p equally among 6 children. How much each?	p
4	Find the sum of 20p, 30p and 45p.	p
5	From 78p take a FIFTY.	p
6	What is the cost of six beads at 7p each?	p
7	Find the difference between 8×5 and 10×8.	
8	Add the even numbers between 23 and 27.	
9	What is the remainder when 28 is divided by 6?	
10	How much greater is $3\frac{1}{4}$ than $2\frac{1}{2}$?	

C

		ANSWER
1	By how many cm is a half metre longer than 34 cm?	cm

2  This clock is 10 minutes slow. Write the correct time in figures. Use a.m. or p.m.

morning

		ANSWER
3	How many FIVES are equal in value to 15 TWOS?	FIVES
4	Write in figures the number which is seven less than one hundred and one.	

5

cm				

How many strips each this length can be cut from a half-metre strip?

		ANSWER
6	If 29th August is a Saturday, what day is 1st September?	
7	If a FIVE and a TWO are saved each week, how much will be saved in 4 weeks?	p
8	In a class of 32 children 17 are girls. How many boys are there?	

9 | 75 83 76 85 |

Which of these numbers is nearest to 80?

10 Divide 12p between Amy and Daniel so that Daniel has twice as much as Amy. How much has Amy? — p

8

Section 1 Test 6

A

		ANSWER
1	100 − 60	
2	28 + 40	
3	5p × 8 = TENS	TENS
4	8 × 4 = 3 tens units	
5	22 + 35	
6	42 ÷ 6 = 10 −	
7	3 TENS − p = 22p	p
8	5p × = 4 TENS + 1 FIVE	
9	34 ÷ 4 = rem.	rem.
10	50p − 26p	p

B

		ANSWER
1	15 plus 18	
2	Find the total of 38 and 42.	
3	What will be the cost of six sweets at 6p each?	p
4	54 cm is divided into 6 equal parts. How long is each part?	cm
5	What is the difference between 14p and 34p?	p
6	What must be added to 37p to make 50p?	p
7	How many threes are equal to 27?	
8	Subtract the product of 6 and 7 from 50.	
9	A metre is divided into 10 equal parts. How long is each part?	cm
10	Subtract 25p from £1.	p

C

		ANSWER
1	Find the cost of 1 badge if 10 badges cost 80p.	p

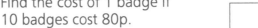

| 2 | Write to the nearest cm the length of the line AB. | cm |

| 3 | What is the total distance round this square? | cm |

$3\frac{1}{2}$ cm

| 4 | Find the cost of $2\frac{1}{2}$ litres when half a litre costs 8p. | p |

5	10 13 17 18 19
	Find the total of the odd numbers.

| 6 | How much less than a FIFTY is the sum of 1 TWENTY and 7 TWOS? | p |

| 7 | A strip half a metre long is cut into 6-cm lengths. How many cm remain? | cm |

| 8 | How many TWENTIES would be given for the money in these two piles? | TWENTIES |

| 9 | Find the difference between $\frac{1}{3}$ of 24 and a quarter of 20. | |

| 10 | This clock is 15 minutes fast. Write the correct time in figures. Use a.m. or p.m. | |

afternoon

9

Section 1 Test 7

A

		ANSWER
1	1800 mℓ = ℓ mℓ	ℓ mℓ
2	25 + 15	
3	1 m 48 cm = cm	cm
4	½ hour + 35 minutes	h min
5	170 + 40	
6	3 TWENTIES − p = 51p	p
7	48 ÷ 5 = rem.	rem.
8	£1 − 46p	p
9	8p × 3 = 2 TENS + TWOS	TWOS
10	24 ÷ 6 = × 4	

B

		ANSWER
1	Multiply 0 by 6.	
2	Subtract 73p from £1.	p
3	6 + 30 + 400	
4	Write 845 to the nearest 100.	
5	What is the remainder when 97 is divided by 10?	
6	How many times heavier is 35 kg than 5 kg?	
7	From 10 times 10 take 5 times 4.	
8	Write the next two numbers in this series. 100, 125, 150, ,	
9	What sum of money is 3 times larger than 15p?	p
10	Add one fifth of 10 to one tenth of 10.	

C

		ANSWER
1	How much change from £1 after buying 10 beads each costing 6p?	p
2	How much further is it from Walsh to Ting than from Ting to Griss?	km
3	35 sweets were shared equally among 6 children. How many sweets were left over?	
4	When two numbers are added together the answer is 45. One of the numbers is 29. What is the other number?	
5	How many quarters of the strip are shaded?	
6	How many complete turns will the minute hand make until the clock shows 9.15?	
7	Tom has 9p left which is one quarter of his spending money. How much had he at first?	p
8	How many times is the six in 69 greater than the six in 96?	
9	badges — large 8p, small 4p — How much would it cost altogether for 5 large and 5 small badges?	p
10	If 10 plums can be bought for 80p, what will be the cost of 3 plums?	p

For C2: 41 km (Walsh to Ting), 25 km (Ting to Griss)

Section 1   Test 8

A

		ANSWER
1	118 cm = 1 metre ▢ cm	cm
2	5 × 7 = 30 + ▢	
3	85p = ▢ TENS + 1 FIVE	TENS
4	$\frac{3}{4} + \frac{3}{4}$	
5	$\frac{1}{2}$ kg − 300 g = ▢ g	g
6	20 FIVES = ▢ TWENTIES	TWENTIES
7	820 − 40	
8	24 cm + 36 cm = $\frac{1}{2}$ m + ▢ cm	cm
9	49 ÷ 6 = ▢ rem. ▢	rem.
10	1 hour − 35 min = ▢ min	min

B

		ANSWER
1	Increase 52 by 18.	
2	1 metre minus 63 cm	cm
3	5 more than 3 sixes	
4	47 more than 28	
5	35 cm less than $\frac{1}{2}$ metre	cm
6	Write the next two numbers in this series. 12, 18, 24, 30, ▢ , ▢	
7	One fifth of a number is 9. Find the number.	
8	Multiply 9 by 6 and add 5.	
9	Find the change from a FIFTY after spending 38p.	p
10	Divide the sum of 24 and 8 by 4.	

C

		ANSWER

1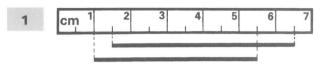

Find the difference in length between the two lines. → cm

2 What is the change from 3 TWENTIES after spending 53p? → p

3 Write to the nearest 10 the sum of 35 and 23. → ▢

4  How many fewer small squares are there in the rectangle than in the large square? → ▢

5 A boy drinks $\frac{1}{2}$ litre of milk each day. How many litres does he drink in two weeks? → ℓ

6 Add $\frac{1}{5}$ of 35 to $\frac{1}{2}$ of 16. → ▢

7 Two biscuits cost 18p. How much do three of the biscuits cost? → p

8

Amy's Savings		
TENS	FIVES	TWOS
2	2	2

Amy wishes to save 50p. How much more does she need? → p

9 There are 100 pages in a book. Emily read 28 pages on Monday and 32 pages on Tuesday. How many more pages are there left to read? → ▢

10 2 TWENTIES and a TWO are divided equally among 6 children. How much does each child receive? → p

Section 1　Test 9

A

		ANSWER
1	300 + 60 + 5	
2	6 × 4 = ▢ × 6	
3	1 kg − 200 g	g
4	34 + 37	
5	45 min + 20 min = ▢ h ▢ min	h　min
6	(7 × 4) + 3	
7	£1 − 53p = ▢ p	p
8	9p × 6 = 5 TENS + ▢ p	p
9	70 cm + 60 cm = 1 m ▢ cm	cm
10	40 ÷ 6 = ▢ rem. ▢	rem.

B

		ANSWER
1	Write three hundred and forty-nine in figures.	
2	How much longer is 1 metre than 57 cm?	cm
3	Increase $\frac{1}{2}$ kg by 250 g.	g
4	350 mℓ less than 1 litre.	mℓ
5	What number is 4 times greater than 9?	
6	£1 minus the sum of 1 TWENTY 2 TENS and 8 FIVES.	p
7	Add the odd numbers between 28 and 32.	
8	How many FIVES are equal in value to 25 TWOS?	FIVES
9	Find the difference between 6 × 5 and 6 × 2.	
10	Write as £s the cost of twenty-five 4p toffees.	£

C

		ANSWER
1	How many FIVES are equal in value to 80p?	FIVES
2	$\boxed{41 \quad 60 \quad 57 \quad 33 \quad 84}$ Which two of these numbers can be divided exactly by 2 without a remainder?	▢ ▢
3	How many days altogether in March and April?	

4

Write to the nearest 10 kilometres the distance represented by the line.　　km

5	Which 4 coins together make 10p?	p　p ⟋ p　p
6	What fraction of 30p is 5p?	

7

This clock is 20 minutes slow. Write the correct time in figures. Use a.m. or p.m.

morning

8	Tom had 27p. He spent $\frac{1}{3}$ of his money. How much had he left?	p
9	Find the cost of 100 grams if $\frac{1}{2}$ kg costs 40p.	p
10	What is the smallest number that can be divided by 2, 3 and 4 without leaving a remainder?	

Section 1   Test 10

A | ANSWER

1	Write 176p as £s.	£
2	30 cm × 4 = 1 m + ☐ cm	cm
3	$\frac{1}{4}$ hour + 20 min	min
4	£1 − 81p	p
5	3 FIVES = ☐ TWOS + 1p	TWOS
6	25 + 66	☐
7	8p × 6 = 1 FIFTY − ☐ p	p
8	1 km − 450 m = ☐ m	m
9	23 ÷ 6 = ☐ rem.	rem.
10	300 mℓ + 330 mℓ = $\frac{1}{2}$ ℓ + ☐ mℓ	mℓ

B | ANSWER

1	Find the sum of 8 and 492.	☐
2	Decrease 205 by 10.	☐
3	Which number is 4 times greater than 19?	☐
4	Write the next two numbers in this series. 250, 300, 350, ☐ ,	☐ ☐
5	How many grams in one tenth of a kilogram?	g
6	Find the total of $4\frac{1}{2}$ ℓ, $7\frac{1}{2}$ ℓ and 15 ℓ.	ℓ
7	Write in figures the sum of one hundred and eighty and twenty-one.	☐
8	How much less is the product of 6 and 5 than 49?	☐
9	Find the cost of 3 drinks costing 25p each.	p
10	Divide £2·00 by 10.	p

C | ANSWER

1	Name the fifth month of the year.	_____
2	How many FIVES are equal in value to 2 TWENTIES?	FIVES
3	Which of the following angles is a right angle?	☐

W   X   Y   Z

4	Find the change from a FIFTY after buying 3 boxes costing 9p each.	p

5

Hoton   Tigby   Cater

35 km

72 km

How far is it from Tigby to Cater? ☐ km

6	Write in figures the number which is ten times one hundred.	☐
7	How much more than $\frac{1}{2}$ of this rectangle is shaded?	☐
8	Which 4 coins together make 36p?	p | p | p | p
9	BADGES 5 for 20p — How much do 20 badges cost?	p
10	Ten cards cost 60p. How much would three cards cost?	p

Section 1 Test 11

A

		ANSWER
1	(3 × 7) + 6	
2	200 + ___ + 8 = 238	
3	£1 − ___ p = 72p	p
4	11.30 a.m. to 12.15 p.m. = ___ min	min
5	37 ÷ 5 = ___ rem.	rem.
6	1 kg − 650 g = ___ g	g
7	£2 = ___ FIVES	FIVES
8	17 + 18 + 5	
9	24 ÷ 3 = ___ × 4	
10	4 TENS + 8 TWOS = ___ p	p

B

		ANSWER
1	By how much is 57p less than £1?	p
2	Find the total cost of 6 packets each costing 15p.	p
3	How many quarters are there in 3 whole ones?	
4	How many pence have the same value as £2·04?	p
5	Which number other than 1, 3 and 27 divides exactly into 27?	
6	How many TENS have the same value as £1·50?	TENS
7	Find the difference between 200 and 20.	
8	Write 450 to the nearest hundred.	
9	Add the odd numbers between 48 and 52.	
10	(a) How many 6p buttons can be bought with a FIFTY? (b) What coin is given in change?	(a) ___ (b) ___ p

C

		ANSWER
1	How many £1 coins have the same value as 300p?	

2 Find the difference in cost between the cheapest and the dearest of these books. [___ p]

 95p £1 39p 65p

3 If 28th September is on a Friday, what is the date the following Monday? _____

4

 V W X Y Z

Which of the shapes is
(a) a rectangle
(b) a triangle?

(a) ___ (b) ___

5 It takes George 35 minutes to walk to school.
At what time must he start from home to arrive at school at 8.50 a.m.? [___]

6 How much less than $\frac{1}{2}$ kilogram is the total mass of 6 packets each having a mass of 80 g? [___ g]

7 Find one third of the sum of 8p and 19p. [___ p]

8 Katie has 25p. Tom has twice as much. How much have they altogether? [___ p]

9 Add one fifth of a FIFTY to one tenth of a FIFTY. [___ p]

10 Write the missing signs
+, −, × or ÷ in place of ● and ▲.
3 ● 7 = 20 ▲ 10   ○ △

Section 1   Test 12

A

		ANSWER
1	$(7 \times 4) + 3$	
2	$\frac{1}{2}$ km + 400 m = m	m
3	$\frac{1}{10}$ of 1 litre = mℓ	mℓ
4	10.15 a.m. to 2.15 p.m. = h	h
5	28 cm + 42 cm = $\frac{1}{2}$ m + cm	cm
6	$54 \div 6 =$ $\times 3$	
7	3 TWENTIES = FIVES	FIVES
8	50p − 32p	p
9	$6p \times 7 = 4$ TENS + p	p
10	£1·20 = TWENTIES	TWENTIES

B

		ANSWER
1	Add 15, 0 and 26.	
2	How much longer is half a metre than 27 cm?	cm
3	Add 3 TENS and 4 FIVES.	p
4	How many FIVES are equal in value to 75p?	FIVES
5	Find the remainder when 106 is divided by 10.	
6	How much shorter is 90 cm than 1 m 20 cm?	cm
7	Take the total of 9 FIVES from £1.	p
8	Subtract 5 from 202.	
9	Find the change from a FIFTY after spending 28p and 18p.	p
10	Decrease four hundred and thirty by fifty. Write the answer in figures.	

C

ANSWER

1 Which of the triangles contains a right angle?

2 How much must be added to 830 grams to make 1 kg?   g

3 How many oranges must be bought to give 11 children half an orange each?

4 The distance round a square is 28 cm. What is the total length of three sides?   cm

5 Write the sum of 500, 50 and 5 to the nearest 10.

6 Find the change from £1 after buying 10 beads each costing 6p.   p

7 This clock is half an hour fast. Write the correct time in figures using a.m. or p.m.

afternoon

8 There are 18 sweets in half a packet of sweets. How many sweets are there in a quarter of the packet?

9 8 children out of a class of 36 are absent. The remainder are divided into 4 equal groups. How many are there in each group?

10 Find the missing signs +, −, × or ÷ in place of ● and ▲
$9 \bullet 3 = 30 \blacktriangle 3$ ○△

Next work Progress Test 1 on page 16.
Enter the result and the date on the chart.

15

PROGRESS TEST 1

Write the numbers 1 to 20 down the side of a sheet of paper.
Write alongside these numbers the **answers only** to the following questions.
Work as quickly as you can. Time allowed – **10 minutes.**

1   18 + 0 + 17

2   Subtract 28p from a FIFTY.

3   Multiply 9 by 4.

4   Find the remainder when 93 is divided by 10.

5   400 + 50 + 9

6   What is the sum of 7 and 299?

7   Which of these numbers can be divided by both 2 and 3 without
a remainder?   14, 15, 18, 20, 23

8   By how many cm is the total of 36 cm and 34 cm less than 1 metre?

9    Write in figures the time this clock will show in
$1\frac{1}{2}$ hours time. Use a.m. or p.m.

morning

10   One fifth of a boy's pocket money is 15p. How much pocket money
does he receive altogether?

11   How many TENS have the same value as £4·80?

12   If 53 sweets are shared equally among 6 children, how many sweets
will be left over?

13   How much change from £1 do you get after buying two pencils
costing 33p and 28p?

14   [420 ml] [½ litre]   How much less than 1 litre are the total contents of
these two cans?

15   Find the difference in value between £$\frac{1}{10}$ and $\frac{1}{5}$ of 45p.

16   Ali put 8 stamps on each of 6 pages and had 7 stamps left.
How many stamps had he altogether?

17   Out of a present of £1·20 Tom's share is $\frac{3}{4}$ and Katie has the
remainder. How much money does Katie receive?

18   ⑤⑤⑤⑤⑤   ②②②②②②   ①①①
Sita changed these coins for TENS. How many did she get?

19   By how many grams is the total of 200 g, 250 g and 400 g
more than $\frac{1}{2}$ kg?

20   There are two layers of chocolates in this box.
How many chocolates are there altogether?

PROGRESS TEST 1 RESULTS CHART

You will work Progress Test 1 at **four** different times. When you first work the test
    (a) colour the first column to show the number of examples correct out of 20
    (b) enter the date.
Each time you work the test, enter the result and the date in the marked columns.

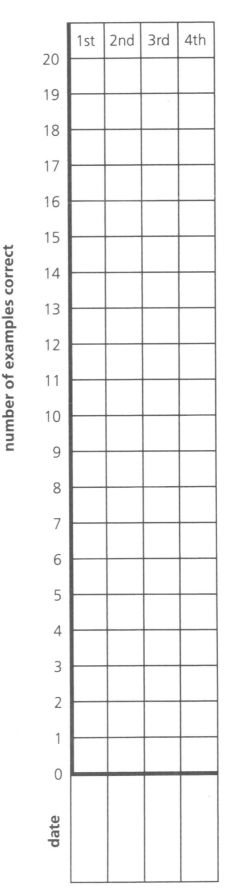

Section 2   Test 1

A | | ANSWER

1 | 600 + 8 + 50 | ☐

2 | Write in figures two hundred and five. | ☐

3 | $1 - \frac{7}{10}$ | ☐

4 | 276p = £ | £ ☐

5 | 540 + 61 | ☐

6 | Write 11 TENS as £s. | £ ☐

7 | 8 × 7 = 50 + | ☐

8 | (a) 1 cm = mm (b) 10 cm = mm | (a) ☐ mm (b) ☐ mm

9 | 2 hours = minutes | ☐

10 | £1 − £0·75 = p | ☐ p

B | | ANSWER

1 | What length remains when 586 mm are divided by 10? | ☐ mm

2 | How many days are there in the sixth month of the year? | ☐

3 | 25 groups of 4. How many altogether? | ☐

4 | Write £2·49 to the nearest £. | £ ☐

5 | Multiply 50 mm by 9. | ☐ mm

6 | Find the difference between $\frac{1}{2}$ km and 370 m. | ☐ m

7 | What is the total of £0·65 and £0·45? | £ ☐

8 | Share £4·00 equally among 8 children. How much each? | ☐ p

9 | Subtract 30 from 501. | ☐

10 | Find the sum of 10 TWENTIES and 5 TENS. | £ ☐

C | | ANSWER

1 | What fraction of the shape is shaded? | ☐

2 | Find the change from £1 after buying 3 litres at 30p per litre. | ☐ p

3 | How many children can each have 10p out of £3·50? | ☐

4 | (1) (2) (1) (5) (5) (5) How much less than 1 TWENTY is the total of the coins? | ☐ p

5 | Tom has £4 and Amy has £1. If they share their money equally, how much does each have? | £ ☐

6 | ⟵ 8 cm ⟶ Write in mm the length of a line 10 times longer than the line above. | ☐ mm

7 | 3 rem. 8 / 9) Find the missing number. | ☐

8 | 131 84 60 49 Add the numbers in the box which can be divided by 2 without a remainder. | ☐

9 | What is the missing number? × 9 = 6 × 3 | ☐

10 | $3\frac{1}{2}$ cm / 7 mm How many times longer is the length of this rectangle than the width? | ☐

18

Section 2   Test 2

A

		ANSWER
1	670 ÷ 10	
2	37 + 73	
3	401 − 6	
4	50 ÷ 7 = rem.	rem.
5	8 × 0 × 7	
6	4 FIFTIES + 5 TWENTIES = £	£
7	£1·86 = TENS + 6p	TENS
8	9p × 8 = TENS + 2p	TENS
9	£1·50 = £1·28 + p	p
10	350 m + $\frac{1}{2}$ km = metres	m

B

		ANSWER
1	Add 15 to 790.	
2	How many sevens are there in sixty-three?	
3	From 310 subtract 30.	
4	What is the cost of 5 kg at 9p for 1 kg?	p
5	How much less than £1·50 is 70p?	p
6	6 metres cost £3·00. What is the cost of 1 metre?	p
7	How many remain when 87 is divided by 9?	
8	25 cm multiplied by 8 = m	m
9	Increase $\frac{1}{2}$ litre by 600 mℓ.	ℓ mℓ
10	Take 29p from 76p.	p

C

		ANSWER
1	One eighth of a number is 5. What is the number?	
2	A half kilogram of meat costs £2·80. What will be the cost of $\frac{1}{4}$ kilogram?	£
3		

GEORGE	ALI
7, 9, 5	8, 7, 9

These are the children's scores in three tests.
How many more in total did Ali score than George?

		ANSWER
4	Divide the sum of 20 and 28 by 8.	
5	How many tenths are equal to (a) one fifth (b) three fifths?	(a) (b)
6	$\overset{6 \text{ rem. } 5}{7\overline{)\,x}}$ What number does x stand for?	
7	By how much is $\frac{1}{3}$ of £1·50 less than $\frac{1}{2}$ of £1·20?	p
8	By how many mm is the distance round square A greater than the distance round square B?	mm
9	Sophie's birthday is in November. Tom's birthday is 4 months later. In which month is Tom's birthday?	_____
10	How many metres less than 10 km is the distance from Mere to Linden as shown on the drawing?	m

Section 2 Test 3

A

		ANSWER
1	3800 mℓ = ☐ ℓ ☐ mℓ	☐ ℓ ☐ mℓ
2	£3·00 − £1·60	£
3	£7 + 5 TENS + 7p	£
4	7 FIFTIES = £ ☐	£
5	(8 × 8) + 6	☐
6	$\frac{1}{4}$ of 1 metre = ☐ cm	☐ cm
7	705 − 40	☐
8	From 9.05 a.m. to 10.25 a.m. = ☐ min	☐ min
9	60 ÷ 7 = ☐ rem. ☐	☐ rem.
10	6 × 6 = 9 × ☐	☐

B

		ANSWER
1	How many times larger is 900 than 9?	☐
2	7 plus 7 plus 7 plus 7	☐
3	Write £1·44 to the nearest 10p.	£
4	What number when multiplied by itself becomes 49?	☐
5	What is the difference between $\frac{1}{4}$ of 800 and $\frac{1}{5}$ of 1000?	☐
6	Add 7 to the product of 6 and 9.	☐
7	How many TWOS are equal in value to 1 TWENTY and 1 TEN?	☐
8	How much more is £2 than £1·13?	£
9	Find the total of £0·67 and 27p.	£
10	How much less than £2·70 are 22 TENS?	£

C

		ANSWER
1	(0 × 3) + (3 − 0) + (0 + 3)	☐
2	Find the change from 9 FIVES after buying 7 sweets costing 6p each.	☐ p
3	How many times greater is $\frac{5}{6}$ of 30 than $\frac{1}{6}$ of 30?	☐
4	How many minutes longer is the Playtime programme than the Cartoons?	☐ min

BBC 1
11.30 Playtime
12.15 Cartoons
12.35 News

5 There were 400 pencils in a box. One eighth of them were blue and the remainder red. How many were there of each colour? blue ☐ red ☐

6 Subtract the sum of the odd numbers from the sum of the even numbers.
(circle contains: 10, 4, 11, 9, 8) ☐

7 How many sweets each weighing 5 grams are there in a box containing $\frac{1}{2}$ kg? ☐

8 By how many mm is a strip measuring 25 cm longer than a strip measuring 220 mm? ☐ mm

9
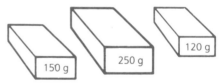
(boxes labelled 150 g, 250 g, 120 g)

How many grams heavier than $\frac{1}{2}$ kg is the total mass of the three boxes? ☐ g

10 Write the missing signs +, −, × or ÷ in place of ● and ▲.
64 ● 8 = 6 ▲ 2 ○ △

Section 2 Test 4

A | | ANSWER

1	689 − 80	
2	$\frac{1}{10}$ of £1 = p	p
3	9p × 10 = 1 FIFTY + TENS	TENS
4	869 = 800 + 9 +	
5	515 ÷ 5 =	
6	5 FIFTIES + 3 TWENTIES	£
7	65 ÷ 7 = rem.	rem.
8	1 km − 110 m = m	m
9	(7 × 9) + 8	
10	43 + 38 = 9 ×	

B | | ANSWER

1	Write in pence the value of the 9 in £8·90.	p
2	Write 2 ℓ 700 mℓ to the nearest litre.	ℓ
3	How many times larger is 220 than 22?	
4	Write the value of 9 FIFTIES.	£
5	What must be added to 360 mℓ to make a half-litre?	mℓ
6	What remains when 50p is divided by 8?	p
7	Subtract 1 m 40 cm from 3 metres.	m cm
8	How many minutes are there from 11.30 a.m. to 12.25 p.m.?	min
9	£2·09 £1·90 £2·10 £0·99 Add the largest of these amounts to the smallest.	£
10	Add the number of days in the 4th and the 5th months of the year.	

C | | ANSWER

1	56 people each bought a ticket costing 10p. Write the total amount paid.	£
2	A plastic strip $1\frac{1}{2}$ metres long is cut into 10 equal pieces. How long is each strip?	cm
3	Three note books cost 50p. What will be the cost of 9?	£
4	If $\frac{1}{3}$ of a number is 18, what is the number?	
5	Katie saved a TEN, a FIFTY and a FIVE. How much less than £1 is that?	p

6

	How much longer in mm is line x than line y?	mm
7	Morning school is from 8.50 a.m. to noon. If there are 20 minutes for play, how many hours and minutes do the children work?	h min
8	Through how many right angles has the minute hand turned since 12 o'clock?	
9	A car uses a litre of petrol to travel 8 km. How many litres will it take to travel 40 kilometres?	ℓ
10	Four children have these amounts of money.	

Amy 8p	Megan 5p	Tom 6p	Sam 9p

	If they put their money together and then share it equally, how much will each child have?	p

Turn back to page 16 and work for the second time Progress Test 1.

Enter the result and the date on the chart.

21

Section 2 Test 5

A | | ANSWER

1	4 + 40 + 400	
2	840 = ⬚ tens	tens
3	18 cm = ⬚ mm	mm
4	Write the missing numbers in this series. 750, 800, 850, 900, ⬚ , ⬚	
5	$\frac{3}{4}$ hour − 20 min = ⬚ min	min
6	(9 × 0) + 3	
7	$2\frac{1}{2}$ kg × 7	kg
8	£3 = ⬚ TWENTIES	TWENTIES
9	(a) $\frac{1}{8}$ of 40 (b) $\frac{3}{8}$ of 40	(a) (b)
10	£1·50 ÷ 6 = ⬚ p	p

B | | ANSWER

1	8 plus 8 plus 8 plus 8	
2	Write 5 m 60 cm to the nearest metre.	m
3	Write the fifteenth of September 1977 in figures.	
4	Multiply 38p by 10.	£
5	How many sevens in seven hundred?	
6	$2\frac{1}{2}$ minus $1\frac{3}{4}$	
7	How much change from a FIFTY after buying six 8p tickets?	p
8	Add 15, 0 and 17.	
9	Find the difference between 19 and 35.	
10	Which number is 9 times larger than 7?	

C | | ANSWER

1	Which of these angles is an obtuse angle?	
2	Find the cost of 150 cm of material at 80p a metre.	£
3	Josh buys 4 biscuits at 9p each. How much change has he from a FIFTY?	p
4	Hassan's father is 36 years old. Hassan is one quarter as old. How old will Hassan be in 5 years time?	
5	Samina had £1's worth of FIVES and £1's worth of TENS. How many coins had she altogether?	
6	Tom is 90 cm tall. Katie is one and a half times his height. How tall is Katie?	cm
7	Harry has £1·50. Jessica has 85p less than Harry. How much has Jessica?	p
8	What is the difference between 10 times 85 and 10 times 100?	
9	$\frac{1}{3}$ of a number is 8. What is $\frac{1}{4}$ of the number?	
10		a	44p		Which amount, a, b or c, can be paid exactly using some of these coins?	
		b	69p			
		c	58p			

22

A

		ANSWER
1	Write the missing numbers in this series. 2150, 2100, 2050, ,	☐ ☐
2	150 + 200 + = 600	☐
3	259 = tens + 9	☐ tens
4	£5·00 − £2·40	£ ☐
5	£4·16 ÷ 4	£ ☐
6	(8 × 6) + 5	☐
7	£0·15 + £0·09 + £0·26 = p	☐ p
8	½ kg costs 10p. Find the cost of 5 kg.	£ ☐
9	(8 × 9) = 7 tens + units	☐
10	¾ of 24p	☐ p

B

		ANSWER
1	How many sixes are equal to 42?	☐
2	4p × 8 = 3 TENS + p	☐ p
3	880 g + 200 g = 1 kg + g	☐ g
4	Divide £3·00 by 10.	☐ p
5	What is the total of 13, 14 and 15?	☐
6	How many pennies have the same value as £4·56?	☐ p
7	Subtract 150 grams from ½ kilogram.	☐ g
8	How many times smaller is 54 than 540?	☐
9	Decrease 1½ metres by 80 cm.	☐ cm
10	1 kg costs 50p. 3½ kg cost £ .	£ ☐

C

		ANSWER
1	How much more is 18p + 17p than 2 × 15p?	☐ p
2	 afternoon — The clock is 20 minutes slow. Write the correct time in figures using a.m. or p.m.	☐
3	$x \overline{)72}$ with 6 above. What does x stand for?	☐
4	 40mm, 20mm — What is the distance round this rectangle?	☐ mm
5	Find the change from £3 after spending £1·40 and 80p.	£ ☐
6	There are 150 children in a school. Two thirds of the children have school meals. How many children is that?	☐
7	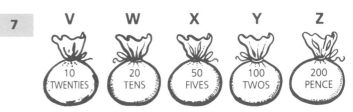 V (10 TWENTIES) W (20 TENS) X (50 FIVES) Y (100 TWOS) Z (200 PENCE) — Which bag contains the most money?	☐
8	1 kg costs 80p. What is the cost of (a) ¼ kg (b) ¾ kg?	(a) ☐ p (b) ☐ p
9	If Christmas Day falls on a Sunday, on which day will New Year's Day fall?	_____
10	Beads are 10 for 30p. How much will 100 beads cost?	£ ☐

Section 2 Test 7

A | ANSWER

1 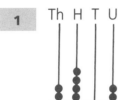 Th H T U Write in words the number shown on the abacus picture.

_____

2 390 mm =   centimetres | cm

3 25 + 78 |

4 2010 − 20 |

5 £1·25 + £2·80 | £

6 (7 × 8) + 6 |

7 51 ÷ 9 =   rem. | rem.

8 £0·12 × 9 | £

9 35 + 29 = 8 × |

10 1 kg costs 45p.
200 g cost   p. | p

B | ANSWER

1 Write ten minutes to nine in the morning in figures. Use a.m. or p.m. |

2 From (8 + 0) take (8 × 0). |

3 Write £2·04 to the nearest TEN. | £

4 Write in figures one and three-quarters. |

5 £5 equals   TWENTIES. | TWENTIES

6 What is the sum of 39, 11 and 15? |

7 What fraction of 25 is 5? |

8 24 plus 14, minus 8. |

9 Write the number which is 7 times larger than 150. |

10 Find (a) $\frac{1}{3}$ of 18p.
       (b) $\frac{2}{3}$ of 18p. | (a)   p | (b)   p

C | ANSWER

1 One side of a street is numbered in even numbers 2, 4, 6, 8 . . . What number is the ninth house? |

2 Find the difference between 3 × 10 and 3 × 100. |

3 What number, other than 1, divides exactly into both 14 and 35? |

4 How many metres less than half a kilometre is 150 metres × 3? | m

5
Hassan

Sophie

How much less has Hassan than Sophie? | p

6 Three numbers total 84. One number is 28 and another 12. What is the third number? |

7 How many cards each costing 25p can be bought for £2·50p? |

8  35cm 25cm 40cm What is the total length of the sides of the triangle in mm? | mm

9 How much change from £1 after buying 8 badges costing 9p each? | p

10 Write the missing signs
+, −, × or ÷ in place of ● and ▲.
4 ● 4 = 9 ▲ 7 | ○ △

Section 2   Test 8

A

		ANSWER
1	Write in figures one thousand and thirty.	
2	$(0 \times 7) + (7 + 0)$	
3	From noon to 12.45 p.m. = ___ min	min
4	£1·00 − £0·35	£
5	Write the missing numbers in this series. 925, 950, 975, ___ , ___	
6	$(4 \times 9) + 7$	
7	$71 \div 8 =$ ___ rem.	rem.
8	4 TWENTIES + 8 FIVES = £ ___	£
9	$\frac{1}{10}$ of $\frac{1}{2}$ metre = ___ cm	cm
10	1 litre costs 60p. $\frac{1}{4}$ litre costs ___ p.	p

B

		ANSWER
1	Find the product of 9 and 7.	
2	Write as mm the sum of 70 cm and 50 cm.	mm
3	How much is one share if £4·20 is divided into seven equal shares?	p
4	How many times smaller is 340 than 3400?	
5	24p + 30p + 63p = £ ___	£
6	How many hours from 9 a.m. to 9 p.m.?	h
7	Take 600 mℓ from $1\frac{1}{2}$ litres.	mℓ
8	What number when multiplied by itself becomes 81?	
9	Subtract 6 times 7 from 50.	
10	Increase £2·50 by $\frac{1}{6}$ of £3·00.	£

C

		ANSWER
1	 Which of these angles is an acute angle?	
2	How many FIFTIES have the same value as the sum of 15 TENS?	FIFTIES
3	Sophie was born in 1990. How old will she be in the year 2030?	
4	How many grams more than 1 kg is the mass of the contents of four of these tins? (300 g Net mass)	g
5	A ribbon 4 m 80 cm long is cut into eight equal pieces. What is the length of one piece?	cm
6	How much shorter is line x than line y?	mm
7	If it costs 25p to travel 5 km, how much will it cost to travel 50 km at the same rate?	£
8	Lucy bought these books. (£1·50, £2·70) How much change was there from £5?	p
9	By how many is $\frac{3}{8}$ of 48 greater than $\frac{1}{8}$ of 48?	
10	Three transfers cost 4p. How many transfers can be bought with 1 TWENTY?	

Turn back to page 16 and work for the third time Progress Test 1.

Enter the result and the date on the chart.

25

Section 2 Test 9

A

ANSWER

1 9 cm × 100 = ▢ m

▢ m

2 ▢ + 150 = 1000

▢

3 1 metre costs 40p.
8 metres cost £ ▢ .

£ ▢

4 1 FIFTY − 17p = ▢ p

▢ p

5 998 + 20

▢

6 9p + 61p + 8p = £ ▢

£ ▢

7 How many minutes from
10.35 a.m. to 11.05 a.m.?

▢ min

8 Write the missing numbers in
this series.
250, 500, 750, ▢ ,

▢ ▢

9 78 ÷ 9 = ▢ rem. ▢

▢ rem. ▢

10 (a) $\frac{1}{8}$ of 56 (b) $\frac{5}{8}$ of 56

(a) ▢ (b) ▢

B

ANSWER

1 How many TENS equal £3·40?

▢ TENS

2 Find the total of £1·35 and
£0·70.

£ ▢

3 $1\frac{1}{2}$ metres divided by 5

▢ cm

4 Write £4·75 to the nearest £.

£ ▢

5 One sixth of a number is 7.
What is the number?

▢

6 How much change from £2
after spending £1·33?

£ ▢

7 By how many is 1250 greater
than 300?

▢

8 Find the total of $\frac{1}{2}$ litre
and 550 ml.

▢ ℓ ▢ mℓ

9 Add 6 to the product of 3
and 9.

▢

10 (8 ÷ 8) plus (0 × 6) plus
(5 − 0)

▢

C

ANSWER

1  Through how
many right angles
has the minute
hand turned
since 11 o'clock?

▢

2 Josh has 28p and Ahmed has
half as much as Josh. How
much have they altogether?

▢ p

3 How many months are there
in 2 years?

▢

4   How many bottles
like this can be
filled from a can
containing 2 litres?

200 mℓ

▢

5 Thomas bought 3 cards costing
24p each.
Find the change from £1.

▢ p

6 ↓
1900 ────── 1950 ────── 2000

The arrow shows the year in
which Grandfather Jones was
born. How old was he in
the year 2000?

▢

7 What must be added to the
sum of 2 TWENTIES and
9 FIVES to make £1?

▢ p

8 $8\overline{)x}$ 7 rem. 4   What is the
value of x?

▢

9 Jamil had 480 cards. He tied
them in bundles of 50.
How many cards were left over?

▢

10 Six sweets cost 8p.
How many can be bought
for 40p?

▢

26

A

		ANSWER
1	3050 − 100	
2	5 × 8 = 10 ×	
3	£1·25 + £0·80	£
4	2300 mℓ = ☐ litres ☐ mℓ	ℓ mℓ
5	93 cm = ☐ mm	mm
6	54 ÷ 7 = ☐ rem.	rem.
7	£2·00 − ☐ p = £1·59	p
8	25 FIVES = £	£
9	(a) $\frac{1}{5}$ of 400 (b) $\frac{3}{5}$ of 400	(a) (b)
10	(8p × 10) + 20p = £	£

B

		ANSWER
1	How many hundreds are there in 1200?	
2	Write 945 cm to the nearest metre.	m
3	Add 6 to the product of 7 and 7.	
4	Find the sum of 75 and 999.	
5	3460 = ☐ × 10	
6	What is the total of £1·45 and £2·55?	£
7	How much change from £5 after spending £3·85?	£
8	How much heavier is $1\frac{1}{2}$ kg than 900 g?	g
9	Three quarters plus a half. Write the answer in figures.	
10	Add $\frac{1}{8}$ of 24 to $\frac{1}{6}$ of 24.	

C

		ANSWER
1	Which of the angles in the drawing is (a) an acute angle (b) an obtuse angle?	(a) (b)
2	The value of $\frac{1}{5}$ of a coin is 10p. What is the value of the coin?	p
3	1300 people attended the school fête. If 800 were adults, how many children were there?	
4	101 tickets costing 5p each were sold. Write the amount taken as £s.	£
5	OFFICE HOURS 9.00 a.m. to 11.30 a.m. 2.00 p.m. to 3.30 p.m. For how many hours is the office open?	h
6	What remains after taking 2 kg 200 g from 4 kg?	kg g
7	How many millimetres are there in one metre?	mm
8	10 pieces each $8\frac{1}{2}$ cm long are cut from a metre of ribbon. What is the length of the remaining piece?	cm
9	$\frac{2}{3}$ $\frac{4}{8}$ $\frac{3}{7}$ $\frac{3}{4}$ $\frac{4}{6}$ $\frac{5}{10}$ Two of these fractions each equal one half. Which are they?	☐ ☐
10	Four transfers cost 9p. How many transfers can be bought for 45p?	

Section 2   Test 11

A   ANSWER

1 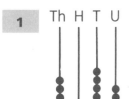 Th H T U   Write in words the number shown on the abacus picture.

_____

2 2400 =   hundreds   ☐

3 £5·00 − £3·99   £ ☐

4 80 min + 40 min =   h   min | h | min |

5 $2\frac{1}{2}$ kg + 600 g =   kg   g | kg | g |

6 $1\frac{1}{10} + \frac{9}{10}$ ☐

7 2 FIFTIES + 4 TWENTIES + 4 FIVES = £   £ ☐

8 (6 × 5) + (8 × 7)   ☐

9 7 metres cost 91p. 1 m will cost   p.   p ☐

10 75 ÷ 8 =   rem. | rem. |

B   ANSWER

1 2000 +   + 6 = 2076   ☐

2 £0·35 + £0·26 + £0·37 =   p   p ☐

3 What number is 100 times greater than 11?   ☐

4 How many millimetres are there in the sum of $7\frac{1}{2}$ cm and $2\frac{1}{2}$ cm?   mm ☐

5 Divide 1040 by 10.   ☐

6 Find the total of 37 and 25.   ☐

7 Write 4 kg 400 g to the nearest kg.   kg ☐

8 (3 × 8) equals (4 ×   )   ☐

9 Subtract 20 plus 16 from 50.   ☐

10   7 rem. 7 Find the value
8)‾x‾   of x.   ☐

C   ANSWER

1 Which of these is a pair of parallel lines?

(a)   (b)   (c)   (d)   (e)   ☐

2 Saba saves 20p each week. How long will it take her to save £4?   ☐

3 A piece of wood is $\frac{1}{2}$ metre long. How many cm does another piece measure which is one and a half times as long?   cm ☐

4  £1·50   How much change from a £5 note after buying three aeroplanes?   p ☐

5 Which of the numbers below can be divided by 9 without a remainder?

| 28 49 56 63 71 | ☐

6 4 cards cost 12p. How much will 12 cards cost?   p ☐

7 | $\frac{1}{4}$ litre $\frac{1}{5}$ litre $\frac{1}{2}$ litre $\frac{1}{10}$ litre |

Add the largest of these quantities to the smallest. Give the answer in millilitres.   m ℓ ☐

8 For her birthday, Katie received 50p, 75p and 25p. How much must her father give her to make the amount up to £2?   p ☐

9  Estimate the number of sweets   There were 900 sweets in the bottle. These were the estimates.

Katie	Ahmed	Amy	Ali
870	926	860	933

Who made the best estimate? _____

10 Flowers cost 70p for 10. What is the cost of 15 flowers?   £ ☐

Turn back to page 16 and work for the fourth time Progress Test 1.

Enter the result and the date on the chart.

28

Section 2 Test 12

A | ANSWER

1 3000 + 6 + 50 + 400 [   ]

2 200 g × 7 =   kg   g [kg   g]

3 (5 cm × 3) − 12½ cm [cm]

4 £4·50 =   TENS [TENS]

5 1 − ⅝ [   ]

6 Find the number of hours from 11.30 a.m. to 3.30 p.m. [h]

7 (7 × 6) + 4 [   ]

8 ⅑ of 27 [   ]

9 6 TWOS + 6 FIVES =   p [p]

10 43 ÷ 9 =   rem. [rem.]

B | ANSWER

1 How many 100s in 4000? [   ]

2 Write 176 mm as cm and mm. [cm   mm]

3 How much greater is (3 × 10) than (4 × 7)? [   ]

4 Share 75p equally among 5 children. What is one share? [p]

5 How much more is £3 than £2·23? [p]

6 Multiply the product of 4 and 5 by 8. [   ]

7 Write 3 km 600 m to the nearest kilometre. [km]

8 Complete this series. 36, 45, 54,   ,   [ ][ ]

9 Find the cost of 1¼ kg if 1 kg costs £0·40. [£]

10 How many minutes from 10.45 a.m. to 11.25 a.m.? [min]

C | ANSWER

1 950 m 850 m
   A   B   C
   How much further than 1½ kilometres is it from A to C? [m]

2 8 parcels each have a mass of 900 g. How many grams less than 7½ kg is this? [g]

3 What is the smallest number that must be added to 74 to make a number exactly divisible by 9? [   ]

4 What fraction of the whole strip is (a) shaded (b) unshaded? [(a)][(b)]

5 Three books were bought costing £1·25, £1·15 and £1·10. What coin was given in change from four £1 coins? [p]

6   JAM 1½kg Net mass
   Half of this large jar of jam was used. How many grams were left? [g]

7 In a £3 bag of TENS and FIVES there are 24 TENS. How many FIVES are there? [FIVES]

8 Two badges and a card cost 35p. If the card costs 15p, how much did each badge cost? [p]

9 | 475 g | 530 g |
   | 480 g | 523 g |
   Which of the masses is nearest to a half kg? [g]

10 | £3·45 | £1·46 | £2·54 | £1·55 |
    Which two amounts in the box total £5? [£][£]

Next work Progress Test 2 on page 30.
Enter the result and the date on the chart.

Next work Progress Test 2 on page 30.

29

PROGRESS TEST 2

Write the numbers 1 to 20 down the side of a sheet of paper.
Write alongside these numbers the **answers only** to the following questions.
Work as quickly as you can. Time allowed – **10 minutes.**

1 18 +   = 31

2 $\frac{1}{8}$ of 56

3 2000 + 300 + 5

4 Subtract 6 from 1005.

5 10 rulers each measuring 30 cm long are placed end to end.
Find the total length of the rulers in metres.

6 How many metres less than $\frac{1}{2}$ km is 380 m?

7 How many TENS are equal in value to £4·30?

8 Write £2·75 to the nearest TEN.

9 Find the difference in millilitres between 675 mℓ and a half-litre.

10 How many days altogether in the 5th and 6th months of the year?

11 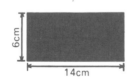 Which two coins must be added to those in the box to make a total of £3?

12 If a half-kilogram of sweets costs 75p, how much will 100 g cost?

13 An office opens at 9.30 a.m. and closes at 4.30 p.m. How many hours is it open?

14 If £4·00 is shared equally among 5 children, how much does each get?

15 How much greater is the distance all round the rectangle than the distance all round the square?
Write the answer in mm.

9½cm   6cm   14cm

16 There were 7 litres of oil in a can. How many litres and mℓ remain when 700 mℓ are used?

17 How many 8-cm lengths can be cut from a strip a half-metre long?

18 How much change from a £5 note after spending £1·50 and £2·30?

19 200m

Sita's home   School

Sita walks to school in the morning and returns in the evening.
How many km does she walk in 5 days?

20 6 parcels of equal mass together have a mass of 1 kg 200 g.
What is the mass of 4 of the parcels?

PROGRESS TEST 2

You will work Progress Test 2 at **four** different times. When you first work the test
   (a) colour the first column to show the number of examples correct out of 20
   (b) enter the date.
Each time you work the test, enter the result and the date in the marked columns.

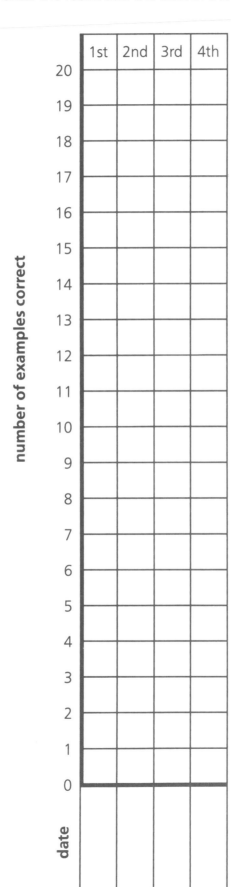

Section 3   Test 1

A | | ANSWER

1 300 + 6000 + 80

2 6940 ÷ 10

3 9 + 9 + 9 + 9 + 9 + 9 + 9

4 Write 4300 g to the nearest kg. | kg

5 $2\frac{1}{2}$ kg − 800 g | kg   g

6 £0·18 × 6 | £

7 $1\frac{1}{2}$ m − 90 cm =   cm | cm

8 £1·00 − 58p | p

9 $\frac{3}{4}$ of 40p | p

10 £1·44 ÷ 9 | p

B | | ANSWER

1 How many hundreds in 3000?

2 Find the sum of £1·15 and £2·85. | £

3 How many TENS are equal in value to 27 TWENTIES?

4 Write 497 to the nearest 10.

5 From £3 take £2·22. | p

6 Find the total cost of 5 cards each costing 22p. | £

7 3407 m = 3 km   m | m

8 What is the product of 9 and 99?

9 Multiply (3 × 3) by 3.

10 From 1070 mm take 20 cm. | mm

C | | ANSWER

1 £1·35 was given in change after spending £3·65. What amount had been given to the shopkeeper? | £

2   35 mm   Find the distance round the square in cm. | cm

3 If 100 grams of chocolate cost 80p, how much will 250 grams cost? | £

4 20 drinks can be made from a bottle of orangeade. How many bottles will be needed for 160 drinks?

5 | 42   47   50   43 |

From the sum of the even numbers in the box subtract the sum of the odd numbers.

6 Hassan spends 24 minutes altogether each day travelling to and from school. How many hours is this from Monday to Friday? | h

7 Sweets are sold at 4 for 5p. How many can be bought with a FIFTY?

8 cm
This line represents 100 km. What do 3 cm on the line represent? | km

9 How much less is $\frac{1}{2}$ of £1·20 than $\frac{3}{4}$ of £1·20? | p

10 700 ml 450 ml 350 ml   1 litre of water has a mass of 1 kilogram.
Find the mass in kg of the water contained in the three jugs. | kg

32

Section 3   Test 2

A | | ANSWER

1	28×10	
2	196 mm = cm mm	cm mm
3	$1 - \frac{3}{8}$	
4	£5 − £4·85	£
5	2 kg 600 g + 800 g	kg g
6	$\frac{1}{4}$ of £4·16	£
7	2 km 90 m = m	m
8	$(7 \times 3) + (7 + 3)$	
9	$8p \times 7 = 60p -$ p	p
10	£4·90 ÷ 7 = p	p

B | | ANSWER

1	Find the change from £2 after spending £1·24.	p
2	What is the product of 8 and 50?	
3	2300 equals 23 times .	
4	 What fraction of the rectangle is shaded?	
5	Write 85 mm to the nearest cm.	cm
6	8 pencils cost 72p. What is the cost of 1?	p
7	How many TWOS are equal in value to 3 TWENTIES?	TWOS
8	Divide 39 by 9.	rem.
9	Find $\frac{2}{3}$ of 60.	
10	Add $1\frac{3}{4}$ and $2\frac{1}{2}$.	

C | | ANSWER

1	 Which of the shapes has two pairs of parallel lines?	
2	At a school concert there were 6 rows each containing 15 chairs. 20 of the chairs were not used. How many chairs were used?	
3	Find the change from a £5 note after buying 1 kg of meat at £2·35 per $\frac{1}{2}$ kg.	p
4	The masses of 3 parcels are 250 g, 300 g, $\frac{1}{2}$ kg. By how many g is the total mass more than 1 kg?	g
5	What is the distance from Y to Z?	km
6	Mandeep was aged 10 in 1990. How old will he be in the year 2020?	
7	A car travelled 300 km at 60 km/h. How long did the journey take?	h
8	10 sweets have a mass of 50 g. How many sweets will have a mass of $\frac{1}{2}$ kg?	
9	The distance round the square is the same as the distance round the triangle. What is the length of one side of the square? 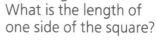	cm
10	Tom's height is 90 cm and Amy is 40 cm taller. How many cm less than $1\frac{1}{2}$ m is Amy's height?	cm

(Item 5 diagram: X — 29 km — Y ——— Z, total 68 km)

33

Section 3   Test 3

A

		ANSWER
1	Write in figures six thousand one hundred and one.	
2	$9 \times 7 = 70 -$	
3	£0·23 + £1·77	£
4	73 − 28	
5	£0·64 ÷ 8 = ☐ p	p
6	Write 378 cm to the nearest metre.	m
7	18 FIVES = ☐ TENS	TENS
8	3 litres 300 mℓ − $\frac{1}{2}$ litre	ℓ ☐ mℓ
9	From 10.35 a.m. to 11.10 a.m. = ☐ min	min
10	$\frac{1}{2}$ km − 397 m	m

B

		ANSWER
1	Complete this series. 4075, 4050, 4025, ☐ , ☐	☐ ☐
2	From the sum of 39 and 6 subtract 20.	
3	From £5 take £3·08.	£
4	Increase £2·50 by 7 TENS.	£
5	Multiply £1·40 by 3.	£
6	Share £1·20 equally among 5 children. How much is one share?	p
7	How many cm in three tenths of a metre?	cm
8	5 pencils cost £1. What is the cost of (a) 1 pencil (b) 4 pencils?	(a) ☐ p (b) ☐ p
9	Find the cost of 4 m of cloth at £0·75 per metre.	£
10	How many mm in $\frac{1}{10}$ m?	mm

C

		ANSWER
1	 Which of the triangles is a right-angled triangle?	
2	James was born in 1968. Harry is 5 years younger. In what year was Harry born?	
3	Leah gave 6 friends 8 sweets each and she had 5 sweets left. How many had she at first?	
4	A ——————————— B Estimate which of these measurements is nearest to the length of the line AB. 10 cm 60 mm $\frac{1}{4}$ m 20 mm	mm
5	Which of these numbers can be divided by both 8 and 9 without a remainder? 38 49 57 72 82	
6	Ellie is 135 cm tall and George is 40 cm smaller. How much short of 1 metre is George's height?	cm
7	 N ↑ Tom's house Sophie's house In what direction must Tom walk to get to Sophie's house?	
8	3 of Hassan's paces measure $1\frac{1}{2}$ m. What do 12 of his paces measure?	m
9	Katie 90p Olivia 90p Chloe 60p The children shared their money equally. How much did each get?	p
10	Sita received 1 TWENTY, 2 FIVES and 2 TWOS in change from £1. How much had she spent?	p

Section 3 Test 4

A   ANSWER

1.   45 min + 25 min =   h   min | h   min |

2.   1009 − 100

3.   4 TWENTIES =   FIVES | FIVES |

4.   600 mℓ × 5 =   ℓ | ℓ |

5.   £0·15 × 8 | £ |

6. $\frac{1}{9}$ of 81p | p |

7.   £4 − £3·77 | £ . |

8.   650 mm =   cm | cm |

9.   16p × 7 = £ | £ |

10. $4\frac{1}{2}$ kg − 700 g | kg   g |

B   ANSWER

1.   Write 114 mm to the nearest cm. | cm |

2.   Write in figures the time shown on this clock. Use a.m. or p.m.

   afternoon

3. | 20   31   54   69 |

   Add the odd numbers in the box.

4.   How many minutes from 9.25 a.m. to 10.20 a.m.? | min |

5.   How much less than 2 whole ones are 5 quarters?

6.   Find the total of 24 and 79.

7.   What fraction of 56p is 7p?

8.   4 sweets cost 20p. How much will 20 cost? | £ |

9.   Divide £1·50 by 6. | p |

10.   What is the missing sum of money?
     p ÷ 3 = 15p | p |

C   ANSWER

1.   In a game Josh scored 50 and 37. How many more did he need to make his score 100.

2.   A roll of ribbon 4 metres long was cut into 20-cm lengths. How many lengths were there?

3. 

   Which of the triangles is an acute-angled triangle?

4.   A queen was born in 1820 and died in 1901. How old was she when she died?

5.   How many right angles are there in a turn from north to south?

6.   2200 cards were put into packets of 10. How many packets were there altogether?

7.   In a money box there were 10 TENS and 9 TWENTIES. How much less than £3 was the total? | p |

8.   £1·50   £1·55   Find the change from £5 after paying these two amounts. | £ |

9.   A cup holds 150 mℓ. How many mℓ are left from 1 litre when 6 cupfuls have been used? | mℓ |

10.   Mandeep's height is $1\frac{3}{4}$ metres. How many cm taller is he than Ali whose height is 110 cm? | cm |

Turn back to page 30 and work for the second time Progress Test 2.

Enter the result and the date on the chart.

Section 3 Test 5

A

		ANSWER
1	5004 = hundreds and 4 units	
2	78 TENS = £	£
3	29 + 38	
4	4 TWENTIES − 74p	p
5	$14\frac{1}{2}$ cm = mm	mm
6	Write in figures, using a.m. or p.m., ten minutes to ten in the morning.	
7	2050 mℓ = ℓ mℓ	ℓ mℓ
8	£3 − 75p	£
9	How many m in (a) $\frac{1}{10}$ km (b) $\frac{1}{5}$ km?	(a) m (b) m
10	61 ÷ 9 = rem.	rem.

B

		ANSWER
1	Subtract 20 from 708.	
2	A FIFTY minus 17p.	p
3	Increase £1·45 by £1·65.	£
4	What is the cost of 25 cm at £1·20 per metre?	p
5	This clock is 20 min fast. Write the correct time in figures. Use a.m. or p.m. morning	
6	Find the total cost of 2 toy cars each costing £1·38.	£
7	How much less than a whole one is the smallest of these fractions? $\frac{1}{2}$ $\frac{1}{7}$ $\frac{1}{4}$ $\frac{1}{10}$ $\frac{1}{3}$	
8	By multiplying find the sum of 29, 29, 29 and 29.	
9	Find $\frac{3}{5}$ of 35.	
10	10 times 10 times 10	

C

		ANSWER
1	A car travels 90 km on 10 litres of petrol. How far will it travel on 30 litres?	km
2	5 packets each contain 50p. How much more than £2 is the total value?	p
3	W X Y Z Which of these triangles is an obtuse-angled triangle?	
4	A car travels at 54 km/h. How far does it travel in (a) 30 min (b) 10 min?	(a) km (b) km
5	700g 850g Y The total mass of the 3 parcels is 2 kg. What is the mass in grams of parcel Y?	g
6	In 2020 Ali's father will be 45 years old. In which year was his father born?	
7	Each day Mrs Gray has 3 half-litres of milk except on Sunday when she has twice as much. How many litres does she have each week?	ℓ
8	cm One cm on this line represents 500 m. How many km does the whole line represent?	km
9	For her birthday Yasmin had 8 TENS and 4 TWENTIES. How much more does she need to buy a toy costing £1·95?	p
10	Find the difference between the sum of 9 and 9 and the product of 9 and 9.	

Section 3 Test 6

A

		ANSWER
1	2784 − 780	
2	15p × 100 = £	£
3	48 + 27	
4	£4 − £3·19	p
5	35p × 3 = £	£
6	1 kg 200 g − $\frac{1}{2}$ kg = g	g
7	7 × 9 = 50 +	
8	$\frac{7}{10}$ of 1 kg = g	g
9	9000 − 1100	
10	£3·48 ÷ 6 = £	£

B

		ANSWER
1	Write 482p as £s.	£
2	Find the cost of 6 comics costing 90p each.	£
3	How much longer is 1687 m than 1$\frac{1}{2}$ km?	m
4	How much greater is 1050 than 700?	
5	Add $\frac{1}{6}$ of 54 to $\frac{1}{3}$ of 27.	
6	3 plus 800 plus 40 plus 5000	
7	$\frac{3}{8}$ of 32	
8	7 × 6 = x + 12 What is the value of x?	
9	(8 × 8) plus (8 + 8)	
10	Find the difference between $\frac{1}{8}$ of 72 and $\frac{1}{9}$ of 72.	

C

		ANSWER
1	Find the difference in mass between the heaviest and the lightest of these boxes.	g
2	Write the missing signs +, −, × or ÷ in place of ● and ▲. 3 ● 7 = 10 ▲ 11 ○△	
3	If Tom faces north and then turns clockwise through three right angles, in which direction does he face?	
4	James has an album containing 24 pages with 10 stamps on each page. He has 15 stamps left over. How many stamps has he altogether?	
5	How many TWENTIES can be exchanged for the sum of 3 TENS, 5 FIVES and 5p?	TWENTIES
6	A petrol tank holds 40 litres when full. The dial shows the amount of petrol left in the tank. (a) What fraction of the full amount is this? (b) How many litres are left?	(a) \\ (b) ℓ
7	5 of Katie's paces measure 300 cm. How many metres do 20 of her paces measure?	m
8	Sam went to the museum at 3.45 p.m. He left 1$\frac{1}{2}$ hours later. At what time did he leave?	
9	What is the distance from Y to Z?	mm
10	Which two of the following, when added together, equal 1$\frac{1}{2}$ kg? 350 g 550 g 750 g 950 g	g \\ g

Section 3   Test 7

A

		ANSWER
1	304p = £	£
2	45 ÷ ☐ = 9	
3	(0 × 6) + (6 − 0)	
4	300 − 18	
5	800 m × 5 = ☐ km	km
6	2017 = ☐ tens 7 units	tens
7	48 ÷ 7 = ☐ rem.	rem.
8	25p × 4 = £	£
9	Write this afternoon time in figures, quarter to five. Use a.m. or p.m.	
10	£1·28 + £0·22 = £2 − £	£

B

		ANSWER
1	Find the difference between 6000 and 600.	
2	How many months in one quarter of a year?	
3	Take 30 cm from $\frac{3}{4}$ metre.	cm
4	How much less than £4 is £3·27?	p
5	Find the total cost of 8 badges each costing 11p.	p
6	£4·96 equals ☐ TENS and 6p.	TENS
7	99 plus 99 plus 99	
8	Add $\frac{1}{6}$ of 42 to $\frac{1}{7}$ of 42.	
9	Find the sum of £0·29 and £2·46.	£
10	How much greater is 8 × 4 than 3 × 8?	

C

		ANSWER
1	 The sum of the sides of the triangle is 60 cm. What is the length of the side AB?	cm
2	Find the difference between $\frac{1}{6}$ of 30 and 6 times 30.	
3	Through how many right angles does the minute hand pass from the time shown on clock A to the time shown on clock B?	
4	Josh's birthday is in January. Hassan's birthday is 3 months earlier. In which month is Hassan's birthday?	
5	The money received at a concert was 170 TENS. These coins were put into bags each containing £5. (a) How many bags of £5 were there? (b) What was the value of the coins left over?	(a) ___ (b) £ ___
6	How much less than a half metre is the distance round the rectangle? [rectangle 18cm by 6cm]	cm
7	What is the cost of 7 sweets if 3 sweets cost 30p.	p
8	[cm scale line] This line represents 300 km. What do 2 cm on the line represent?	km
9	From a cask containing 5 litres these amounts were used. $1\frac{1}{2}$ litres, $\frac{3}{4}$ litre, $2\frac{1}{4}$ litres. How many mℓ were left?	mℓ
10	How many foreign stamps can be bought for 45p if a packet of 4 costs 5p?	

Section 3 Test 8

A

ANSWER

1 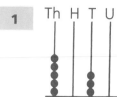 Th H T U   Write in words the number shown on the abacus picture.

_____

2 17 + 6 + ☐ = 31

3 860 mm = ☐ cm ☐ cm

4 £3·25 − £1·75 £ ☐

5 6p × 8 = 4 TENS + ☐ TWOS ☐ TWOS

6 £0·07 × 20 £ ☐

7 $5 - 1\frac{3}{4}$ ☐

8 ☐ p × 8 = £4 ☐ p

9 $\frac{1}{2} + \frac{3}{8}$ ☐

10 96p ÷ 8 ☐ p

B

ANSWER

1 How many pence are equal in value to £3·09? ☐ p

2 Divide the total of 19 and 9 by 7. ☐

3 What is the value of the figure underlined in the number 5306? ☐

4 Write £2·95 to the nearest TEN. £ ☐

5 What fraction of 40p is 5p? ☐

6 How many millilitres must be added to 1 litre 750 mℓ to make 2½ litres? ☐ mℓ

7 If a half kg costs £2·50, how much will 100 g cost? ☐ p

8 Subtract 18 from 65. ☐

9 What is (a) ¼ of 1000 (a) ☐
    (b) ¾ of 1000? (b) ☐

10 In how many months of the year are there 31 days? ☐

C

ANSWER

1 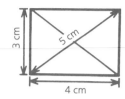 What is the difference between the total length of the two diagonals of the rectangle and the distance all round it? ☐ cm

2 Chloe has a FIFTY each week for pocket money. From this she spends 35p and saves the remainder. How much does she save in 4 weeks? ☐ p

3 At a concert there were 200 children. One quarter of them were girls. How many boys were there? ☐

4   How many right angles are there in a complete turn? ☐

5 Fish costs £4·80 for 1 kg. How much will 1½ kg cost? £ ☐

6

RECEIVED	SPENT
£1·50	£0·30
	£0·65

This is how Daniel keeps an account of his money. How much has he left? £ ☐

7 By how many metres is 1¾ km shorter than 2000 m? ☐ m

8   The total length of the three sides of this triangle is 14 cm. What is the length in mm of the side YZ? ☐ mm

9 Find the difference in cost between 4 small tins at 30p per tin and 2 large tins at 55p per tin. ☐ p

10 How long will it take to travel a distance of 33 km at 6 km/h? ☐ h

Turn back to page 30 and work for the third time Progress Test 2.

Enter the result and the date on the chart.

Section 3 Test 9

A

ANSWER

1 Write in figures the number nine thousand and thirteen.

2 21p × 100 = £ [ ] £

3 4000 = 40 × [ ]

4 (7 × 8) + 5

5 1½ litres − 550 mℓ = [ ] mℓ mℓ

6 4 TWOS + 27p = [ ] FIVES FIVES

7 50p − 17p = [ ] p p

8 750 ÷ 5

9 59 ÷ 7 = [ ] rem. rem.

10 $\frac{3}{10} + \frac{2}{5}$

B

ANSWER

1 Take 200 from 4080.

2 Write 5450 mℓ to the nearest litre. ℓ

3 How many whole ones are equal to 28 quarters?

4 470 g × 10 = [ ] kg [ ] g kg g

5 Find the product of 6 and 23.

6 Decrease 41 by 13.

7 How many minutes from 11.35 a.m. to 12.25 p.m.? min

8 How much less than £4 is £2·72? £

9 Find the difference between 7 × 8 and 6 × 9.

10 Arrange the figures 6, 9, 4 and 8 to make the largest possible number.

C

ANSWER

1 By how much is the sum of £1·15 and 36p less than £2? p

2 Six pieces of wire each measure 9 cm. Find the total length of the pieces in mm. mm

3

200 mm

The diameter of the circle is 20 mm. How many circles can be placed side by side on the strip?

4 6 apples are cut into quarters. How many children can each have three of the pieces?

5

£2·35
£0·07
£1·70

The ticket shows how much Sita spent at the super-market. Find the total amount. £

6 A colour stick costs 8p.
(a) How many can be bought for 60p? (a)

(b) What change will there be? (b) p

7 Katie is at school from 9.00 a.m. until 4.00 p.m. What time remains after taking 2¼ hours for play and dinner time? h

8

| ½ m | ¼ m | 120 cm |
| 80 mm | 20 cm | |

One of the measurements above is the distance all round the square.

Estimate which is the correct measurement. mm

9 8 children each collected 80p and 2 children collected 70p each. How much was this altogether? £

10 Amy had £2·40. She spent $\frac{3}{8}$ of it. How much money had she left? £

40

Section 3   Test 10

A

		ANSWER
1	540 + 70	
2	(3 × 1000) + (6 × 100) + (4 × 10)	
3	9 TENS + 8 FIVES = £	£
4	$\frac{1}{2}$ litre + 650 ml = 1 litre + ml	ml
5	£5 − £ = £3·10	£
6	£2·89 + £0·17	£
7	£1·17 ÷ 9	£
8	44 × 7	
9	$\frac{2}{3}$ of 45p	p
10	9 rem. 4 Find the value $6\overline{)x}$ of x.	

B

		ANSWER
1	7 plus 7 plus 7 plus 7 plus 7	
2	Find the difference between 8 times 9 and 8 times 4.	
3	Find the cost of 8 pens costing 22p each.	£
4	Write 249 cm to the nearest metre.	m
5	How many whole ones equal 40 tenths?	
6	Find the total of 65p and £3·80.	£
7	What must be added to £1·94 to make £3?	£
8	Find $\frac{3}{8}$ of 48.	
9	(45 ÷ 5) minus (18 ÷ 3)	
10	How many $\frac{1}{4}$ litres are there in $3\frac{1}{2}$ litres?	

C

		ANSWER
1	⊢9 cm⊣ What is the distance all round this regular hexagon?	cm
2	From a carton containing 50 kg of sugar, 24 half-kg packets were taken. How many kg of sugar remained?	kg
3	18 27 36 45 54 Which of these numbers can be divided by both 4 and 9 without a remainder?	
4	What will 4 balloons cost if 10 balloons cost £3·00?	£
5	Tom's house Sam's house ⟵ 125 m ⟶ What fraction of a km is walked by Tom when he walks to Sam's house and back again?	km
6	Sugar sticks cost 7p each. (a) How many can be bought for 30p? (b) How much change will there be?	(a) (b) p
7	A prize of £20 was shared among Sam, Megan and Sanjay. Sam had $\frac{5}{10}$ of the money and Megan had $\frac{3}{10}$. How much money did Sanjay receive?	£
8	To $\frac{2}{3}$ of 15p add $\frac{4}{5}$ of 50p.	p
9	1250 ml 450 ml 400 ml The contents of the three cans are put into a bowl. How many millilitres less than $2\frac{1}{2}$ litres is this?	ml
10	A cyclist travelled at the rate of 20 km/h for 6 minutes. How many km did he travel?	km

41

Section 3   Test 11

A

		ANSWER
1	869 ml = $\frac{1}{2}$ litre + ___ ml	___ ml
2	$\frac{7}{10}$ of 1 metre = ___ cm	___ cm
3	48 + 74	___
4	£3·50 − £1·75	£ ___
5	(8 × 5) + (8 × 3)	___
6	$\frac{7}{8} - \frac{1}{2}$ =	___
7	$\frac{1}{2}$ metre = ___ millimetres	___ mm
8	70 ÷ 9 = ___ rem. ___	___ rem.
9	(0 × 10) + (10 × 10) + (10 − 0)	___
10	___ ÷ 6 = 7 rem. 2	___

B

		ANSWER
1	How many fifths of the strip are shaded?	___
2	How many TWENTIES are equal in value to £10?	___ TWENTIES
3	Find the number of days in 7 weeks.	___
4	How many whole ones are equal to 15 fifths?	___
5	How much more is £2·59 than £1·60?	£ ___
6	Apples cost 12p each. How much will 7 cost?	___ p
7	Take 13p from a FIFTY.	___ p
8	5 oranges cost 40p. What will 15 of the oranges cost?	£ ___
9	Find $\frac{3}{4}$ of 32.	___
10	Write in figures, 11 minutes to 7 in the morning. Use a.m. or p.m.	___

C

		ANSWER
1	**DARTS SCORES** Tom: 19, 11, 10 Emily: 20, 13, 17. How many more did Emily score than Tom?	___
2	Find the change out of a FIFTY after paying for $\frac{1}{2}$ kg at 9p for 100 grams.	___ p
3	A train due to arrive at 11.35 a.m. was 40 minutes late. At what time did it arrive?	___
4	3 tins for 45p. How much would 9 of these tins cost?	£ ___
5	In a school of 120 children, 1 in every 20 was absent. How many children were present?	___
6	The radius of the circle is 8 cm. What is the length of the diagonal of the square?	___ cm
7	What is the smallest number that can be divided by 2, 3 and 5 without a remainder?	___
8	Guess the lucky number. Winner 450. In the competition, Sam's guess was 395 and Amy's guess was 510. (a) Who was the nearer and (b) by how many?	(a) ___ (b) ___
9	How many pence less are there in $\frac{3}{8}$ of 40p than in $\frac{5}{8}$ of 40p?	___ p
10	38p 13p 27p 34p. Which of the amounts above could not be paid for exactly using some or all of these coins?	___ p

Section 3   Test 12

A

		ANSWER
1	$\frac{1}{3}$ of £3·09	£
2	(8 × 1000) + (6 × 10) + (9 × 1)	
3	£1·25 × 4	£
4	How many 12s are there in (a) 120 (b) 1200?	(a) (b)
5	1 litre ÷ 4 = mℓ	mℓ
6	6 × 6 = × 9	
7	£1·59 + £0·48	£
8	Complete this series. 3000, 3250, 3500, 3750, ,	
9	Arrange the figures 1, 2, 7, 0 to make the largest possible even number.	
10	÷ 7 = 9 rem. 6	

B

		ANSWER
1	1967 ÷ 10 = rem.	rem.
2	(6 × 0) + (0 + 6) + (6 × 1)	
3	What fraction of 60 is 10?	
4	If $\frac{3}{4}$ of a sum of money is 24p what is $\frac{1}{4}$ of the money?	p
5	The sum of two numbers is 159. One of the numbers is 60. What is the other number?	
6	Multiply $2\frac{1}{2}$ by 6.	
7	Find the cost of $\frac{1}{2}$ kg when 2 kg cost 60p.	p
8	Change 78 TWOS to £s.	£
9	Envelopes cost 8p. What is the cost of (a) 10 (b) 100?	(a) p (b) £
10	What is the remainder when 60 is divided by 7?	

C

		ANSWER
1	£1·75 £1·35 Find the change from a £5 note after paying these two amounts.	£
2	100 cards cost £1. How much will 70 cards cost at the same rate?	p
3	How many more is 1010 minus 100 than 1100 minus 200?	
4	Find the value of the coin which can be exchanged for the sum of 8 TWOS, 6 FIVES and 4p.	p
5	The circumference of this wheel is 200 cm. How many times will it turn in travelling 100 metres?	
6	How many days are there in the first 2 months of a leap-year?	
7	Subtract the product of seven and seven from the product of eight and eight.	
8	Prices of washing-up liquid in three different containers are shown below. Which is the cheapest per litre, A, B or C? A $\frac{1}{2}$ litre 40p B 200 mℓ 15p C 250 mℓ 18p	
9	Find the cost of $1\frac{3}{4}$ metres if 1 metre costs £2.	£
10	How many packets of sweets each containing 250 g can be filled from a box containing $4\frac{1}{2}$ kg?	

Turn back to page 30 and work for the fourth time Progress Test 2.

Enter the result and the date on the chart.

CHECK-UP TEST　Number

A　Write in words the number shown on each abacus picture.

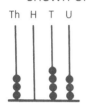 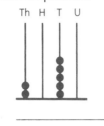

| Th H T U | Th H T U |

_____

_____

B

	a		b	
Take 1 from	900	☐	2000	☐
Add 1 to	499	☐	3999	☐
Take 10 from	6000	☐	5005	☐
Add 10 to	894	☐	7095	☐
Take 100 from	1001	☐	4060	☐
Add 100 to	7049	☐	6990	☐

C　Write in figures

two thousand nine hundred ☐　　one thousand and fifty ☐　　four thousand and eight ☐

D　Write the value of the figure underlined in each number.

8010 ☐　　3284 ☐
2966 ☐　　8304 ☐
4075 ☐　　1090 ☐
5124 ☐　　5007 ☐

E

862 = ▨ tens 2 units ☐
2307 = ▨ tens 7 units ☐
470 = ▨ hundreds 7 tens ☐
6850 = ▨ hundreds 5 tens ☐
4605 = ▨ hundreds 5 units ☐

F　Add

1000 + 500 + 70 + 5　☐
3000 + 60 + 4　☐
4000 + 80　☐
9 + 6000　☐

G　How many times larger is

150 than 15　☐
200 than 2　☐
600 than 60　☐
3000 than 30?　☐

How many times smaller is

12 than 120　☐
70 than 700　☐
59 than 590　☐
42 than 4200?　☐

Addition

H
8 + 5 ___
7 + 6 ___
2 + 9 ___
8 + 8 ___
6 + 6 ___
3 + 9 ___
8 + 7 ___
9 + 9 ___
8 + 4 ___
9 + 5 ___
7 + 7 ___
6 + 9 ___
9 + 8 ___
7 + 4 ___
3 + 8 ___
7 + 5 ___
8 + 6 ___
4 + 9 ___
6 + 5 ___
9 + 7 ___

I
19 + 4 ___
5 + 17 ___
16 + 6 ___
9 + 18 ___
19 + 7 ___
5 + 18 ___
29 + 6 ___
8 + 24 ___
38 + 3 ___
7 + 37 ___
49 + 2 ___
7 + 44 ___
58 + 8 ___
5 + 59 ___
65 + 5 ___
6 + 68 ___
79 + 9 ___
8 + 77 ___
83 + 9 ___
7 + 86 ___

Subtraction

J
16 − 9 ___
11 − 7 ___
14 − 8 ___
13 − 7 ___
17 − 9 ___
11 − 8 ___
12 − 9 ___
13 − 6 ___
15 − 8 ___
13 − 9 ___
12 − 6 ___
15 − 9 ___
14 − 7 ___
13 − 8 ___
12 − 7 ___
14 − 5 ___
12 − 4 ___
11 − 6 ___
12 − 8 ___
18 − 9 ___

K
22 − 4 ___
24 − 7 ___
21 − 6 ___
26 − 9 ___
24 − 8 ___
35 − 9 ___
31 − 5 ___
37 − 8 ___
43 − 5 ___
44 − 9 ___
52 − 3 ___
53 − 7 ___
62 − 9 ___
63 − 4 ___
71 − 8 ___
72 − 6 ___
81 − 7 ___
85 − 8 ___
91 − 4 ___
98 − 9 ___

Tables 2, 3, 4, 5, 6, 7, 8, 9

Multiplication   Division

A		**B**		**C**		**D**	
9×3	___	$(3 \times 4) + 3$	___	$14 \div 7$	___	$11 \div 2$ ___ rem. ___	
4×8	___	$(0 \times 8) + 7$	___	$24 \div 4$	___	$19 \div 4$ ___ rem. ___	
0×3	___	$(8 \times 4) + 3$	___	$40 \div 8$	___	$14 \div 3$ ___ rem. ___	
9×6	___	$(5 \times 7) + 6$	___	$63 \div 9$	___	$16 \div 9$ ___ rem. ___	
3×5	___	$(1 \times 6) + 5$	___	$30 \div 5$	___	$17 \div 3$ ___ rem. ___	
7×6	___	$(6 \times 4) + 3$	___	$18 \div 3$	___	$15 \div 4$ ___ rem. ___	
0×5	___	$(2 \times 8) + 5$	___	$0 \div 2$	___	$12 \div 7$ ___ rem. ___	
7×8	___	$(5 \times 6) + 4$	___	$8 \div 8$	___	$19 \div 2$ ___ rem. ___	
3×7	___	$(8 \times 8) + 7$	___	$54 \div 6$	___	$22 \div 4$ ___ rem. ___	
9×5	___	$(2 \times 6) + 4$	___	$27 \div 9$	___	$29 \div 5$ ___ rem. ___	
6×3	___	$(8 \times 5) + 2$	___	$8 \div 2$	___	$21 \div 8$ ___ rem. ___	
7×9	___	$(7 \times 7) + 5$	___	$56 \div 7$	___	$26 \div 3$ ___ rem. ___	
5×5	___	$(1 \times 8) + 4$	___	$35 \div 5$	___	$36 \div 8$ ___ rem. ___	
0×7	___	$(2 \times 9) + 6$	___	$0 \div 6$	___	$48 \div 5$ ___ rem. ___	
6×6	___	$(7 \times 4) + 3$	___	$36 \div 4$	___	$46 \div 6$ ___ rem. ___	
9×4	___	$(2 \times 7) + 6$	___	$18 \div 2$	___	$41 \div 7$ ___ rem. ___	
0×9	___	$(8 \times 9) + 7$	___	$28 \div 7$	___	$53 \div 6$ ___ rem. ___	
6×8	___	$(0 \times 6) + 4$	___	$81 \div 9$	___	$52 \div 7$ ___ rem. ___	
1×4	___	$(4 \times 4) + 3$	___	$16 \div 4$	___	$70 \div 8$ ___ rem. ___	
8×3	___	$(9 \times 9) + 8$	___	$21 \div 3$	___	$80 \div 9$ ___ rem. ___	

E   What fraction of each of the shapes is   (a) shaded   (b) unshaded?

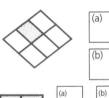

(a)   (b)   (a)   (b)   (a)   (b)   (a)   (b)   (a)   (b)   (a)   (b)

F   Write in figures.

one and a half	☐	two and three-quarters	☐	three and three-fifths	☐	four and two-thirds	☐

G

$1 = \dfrac{\square}{2}$	$\frac{1}{3} + \frac{1}{3} =$ ☐	$1 - \frac{3}{4} =$ ☐	$\frac{1}{8} + \frac{1}{4} =$ ☐	$\frac{3}{4} - \frac{1}{2} =$ ☐
$1 = \dfrac{\square}{4}$	$\frac{3}{5} + \frac{1}{5} =$ ☐	$1 - \frac{5}{8} =$ ☐	$\frac{1}{5} + \frac{1}{10} =$ ☐	$\frac{3}{8} - \frac{1}{4} =$ ☐
$1 = \dfrac{\square}{8}$	$\frac{1}{10} + \frac{2}{10} =$ ☐	$1 - \frac{2}{3} =$ ☐	$\frac{1}{4} + \frac{5}{8} =$ ☐	$\frac{3}{5} - \frac{3}{10} =$ ☐
$1 = \dfrac{\square}{5}$	$\frac{3}{10} + \frac{4}{10} =$ ☐	$1 - \frac{7}{10} =$ ☐	$\frac{1}{2} + \frac{3}{8} =$ ☐	$\frac{5}{6} - \frac{2}{3} =$ ☐

H   Find the value of

$\frac{1}{2}$ of 18p	___ p	$\frac{1}{4}$ of 20 ℓ	___ ℓ	$\frac{1}{5}$ of 40 m	___ m	$\frac{1}{6}$ of 30p	___ p
$\frac{1}{4}$ of 24 kg	___ kg	$\frac{3}{4}$ of 20 ℓ	___ ℓ	$\frac{4}{5}$ of 40 m	___ m	$\frac{5}{6}$ of 30p	___ p
$\frac{1}{10}$ of 60 cm	___ cm	$\frac{1}{8}$ of 32 cm	___ cm	$\frac{1}{10}$ of £1	___ p	$\frac{1}{3}$ of 90 kg	___ kg
$\frac{1}{3}$ of 27p	___ p	$\frac{7}{8}$ of 32 cm	___ cm	$\frac{9}{10}$ of £1	___ p	$\frac{2}{3}$ of 90 kg	___ kg

CHECK-UP TEST　Money

A

£1 = ☐ FIFTIES

£1 = ☐ TWENTIES

£1 = ☐ TENS

£1 = ☐ FIVES

£1 = ☐ TWOS

£1 = ☐ pennies

1 FIFTY = ☐ TENS

1 FIFTY = ☐ FIVES

1 FIFTY = ☐ TWOS

1 TWENTY = ☐ TENS

1 TWENTY = ☐ FIVES

1 TWENTY = ☐ TWOS

£1·48 = £1 + ☐ p

£2·09 = £2 + ☐ p

£0·63 = £0 + ☐ p

£2·80 = £2 + ☐ p

157p = £ ☐

260p = £ ☐

309p = £ ☐

B　Find the change.

Amount	Money spent	Change
10p	4p	p
10p	5p	p
10p	7p	p
15p	11p	p
15p	13p	p
20p	5p	p
20p	8p	p
20p	13p	p

Amount	Money spent	Change
50p	17p	p
50p	38p	p
50p	24p	p
50p	11p	p
50p	27p	p
50p	19p	p
80p	76p	p
90p	81p	p

Amount	Money spent	Change
£1	24p	p
£1	68p	p
£1	85p	p
£1	43p	p
£1	91p	p
£5	£4·62	p
£5	£2·30	£
£5	£3·09	£

C　By counting, find the total value of the coins in each box.

☐ p

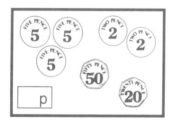

☐ p

☐ p

£ ☐

D

Divide 54p by 9. ☐ p

Reduce 67p by 19p. ☐ p

Find the sum of 23p and 17p. ☐ p

What is the total of 68p and 9p? ☐ p

Multiply 14p by 5. ☐ p

Find the difference between
£0·57 and 75p ☐ p

Add 24p to 66p. ☐ p

How much greater is £1 than 38p? ☐ p

18p plus 12p minus 10p. ☐ p

Subtract 41p from 90p. ☐ p

E

Write to the nearest TEN.　34p ☐ p　£0·86 ☐ p　£1·95 £ ☐　£3·07 £ ☐

Write to the nearest £1.　£1·80 £ ☐　£3·30 £ ☐　£2·25 £ ☐　£4·50 £ ☐

CHECK-UP TEST   Measures

A
20 mm = __ cm
100 mm = __ cm
230 mm = __ cm
320 mm = __ cm

B
135 cm = _ m __ cm
280 cm = _ m __ cm
307 cm = _ m __ cm
199 cm = _ m __ cm

C
3500 m = _ km ___ m
2900 m = _ km ___ m
4270 m = _ km ___ m
1050 m = _ km ___ m

D
4 kg 500 g = ____ g
3 kg 250 g = ____ g
1 kg 100 g = ____ g
2 kg 50 g = ____ g

E
2 ℓ 400 mℓ = _____ mℓ
3 ℓ 250 mℓ = _____ mℓ
4 ℓ 50 mℓ = _____ mℓ
1 ℓ 90 mℓ = _____ mℓ

F
8 cm   = __ mm
7 m 50 cm = ___ cm
3750 g ·   = _ kg ___ g
1460 mℓ   = _ ℓ ___ mℓ

G
½ kilogram = ___ g
¼ kilogram = ___ g
¾ kilogram = ___ g
1/10 kilogram = ___ g
⅕ kilogram = ___ g

½ litre = ___ mℓ
¼ litre = ___ mℓ
¾ litre = ___ mℓ
1/10 litre = ___ mℓ
⅕ litre = ___ mℓ

½ kilometre = ___ m
¼ kilometre = ___ m
¾ kilometre = ___ m
1/10 kilometre = ___ m
⅕ kilometre = ___ m

H

Write to the nearest cm.   29 mm [cm]   32 mm [cm]   77 mm [cm]   85 mm [cm]

Write to the nearest m.   485 cm [m]   300 cm [m]   509 cm [m]   550 cm [m]

Write to the nearest kg.   1 kg 200 g [kg]   2 kg 690 g [kg]   3 kg 250 g [kg]   4 kg 500 g [kg]

I   Find the cost of

6 m at 15p per metre   __ p
3½ m at 20p per metre   __ p
50 cm at 90p per metre   __ p
25 cm at 40p per metre   __ p
1¼ m at 60p per metre   __ p

5 kg at 14p per kg   __ p
2½ kg at 30p per kg   __ p
¼ kg at £1·20 per kg   __ p
100 g at £1·00 per kg   __ p
200 g at 40p per kg   __ p

3 litres at 30p per ℓ   __ p
500 mℓ at 50p per ℓ   __ p
100 mℓ at £2 per ℓ   __ p
1½ litres at 30p per ½ ℓ   __ p
250 mℓ at 70p per ½ ℓ   __ p

J   Write in figures the time shown on each clock using a.m. or p.m.

    morning
times

_____

afternoon
times

_____

K

How many days in		
December	[ ]	
September	[ ]	
August	[ ]	
November	[ ]	
March?	[ ]	

1 hour = [ ] min
½ h = [ ] min
¼ h = [ ] min
¾ h = [ ] min
1 day = [ ] hours
1 week = [ ] days

How long is it from
8.45 a.m. to 9.10 a.m.   [ ] min
3.54 p.m. to 4.20 p.m.   [ ] min
10.56 a.m. to 12.15 p.m.   [ ] h [ ] min
11.38 a.m. to midday   [ ] min
9.00 a.m. to 3.00 p.m.?   [ ] h

47

Schofield & Sims

the long-established educational publisher specialising in maths, English and science

Essential Mental Arithmetic 2

Essential Mental Arithmetic, which has already delivered outstanding results in many schools, gives all students the skills and confidence they need to use maths effectively in everyday situations – whether at school, at work or in other aspects of daily life. Ideal for regular and intensive use, the carefully differentiated questions develop students' functional maths skills to their full potential, giving plenty of opportunities for practice and helping them to become fully numerate.

Every **Essential Mental Arithmetic** book is divided into three sections, each comprising 12 one-page tests presented in a standard format that students will quickly become familiar with. Each test in **Essential Mental Arithmetic 2** contains:
- **Part A:** 10 questions where use of language is kept to a minimum – based on the signs = ,+, −, × and ÷
- **Part B:** 10 questions using number vocabulary – particularly the language associated with the four signs
- **Part C:** 10 questions presented in word form as one- or two-stage problems.

A useful **Language of Maths** glossary on the inside front cover helps to develop students' number vocabulary. Two 10-minute **Progress Tests** are provided, with accompanying **Results Charts**, and final **Check-up Tests** on number, money and measures help student and teacher to identify any gaps in understanding.

The complete range of student books is listed below.

Essential Mental Arithmetic 1	978 07217 1194 2	**Essential Mental Arithmetic 4**	978 07217 1197 3
Essential Mental Arithmetic 2	978 07217 1195 9	**Essential Mental Arithmetic 5**	978 07217 1198 0
Essential Mental Arithmetic 3	978 07217 1196 6	**Essential Mental Arithmetic 6**	978 07217 1199 7

Additional materials for teachers include:
- an entry test, to help you determine the level at which a new student is working; this is downloadable from the **Essential Mental Arithmetic** page on the Schofield & Sims website
- separate books of answers (one per student book), for quick and easy marking; these were written for the original **Schofield & Sims Mental Arithmetic series** but are fully compatible.

For further details, visit www.schofieldandsims.co.uk

This edition copyright © Schofield and Sims Ltd, 2010
Third impression 2012
Based on **Schofield & Sims Mental Arithmetic 2**, compiled by J. W. Adams and R. P. Beaumont, and edited by T. R. Goddard; copyright © Schofield & Sims Ltd, 1976

British Library Cataloguing in Publication Data:
A catalogue record for this book is available from the British Library.

Front cover design and redesign of selected pages by Ledgard Jepson, Sheffield, and Wyndeham Gait Ltd, Grimsby
Printed in the UK by Wyndeham Gait Ltd, Grimsby, Lincolnshire

ISBN 978-07217-1195-9

Schofield & Sims

Dogley Mill, Fenay Bridge, Huddersfield HD8 0NQ
Phone: 01484 607080 Facsimile: 01484 606815
E-mail: sales@schofieldandsims.co.uk
www.schofieldandsims.co.uk

ISBN 978 07217 1195 9
£2.95
(Retail price)